Disney
POCKET STORIES

PANINI PUBLISHING

Written by: Mark Waid
Art by: Marcio Takara
Colours: Andrew Dalhouse
Letters: Jose Macasocol, Jr.

Editor: Paul Morrissey
Trade Editor: Aaron Sparrow
Cover Artist: Marcio Takara
Colours by: Andrew Dalhouse

CHAPTER ONE

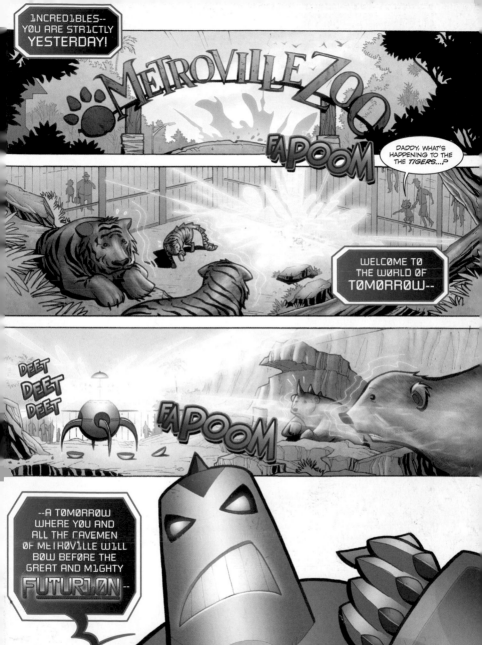

--AND H1S D1N0SAUR ARMY!

13

HMMM.

THIS IS JUST LIKE FUTURION, THOUGH...

...WAIT UNTIL ALL THE ZOOKEEPERS HAVE GONE *HOME*, AND THEN SET OFF ONE LAST *BOOBY-TRAP...!*

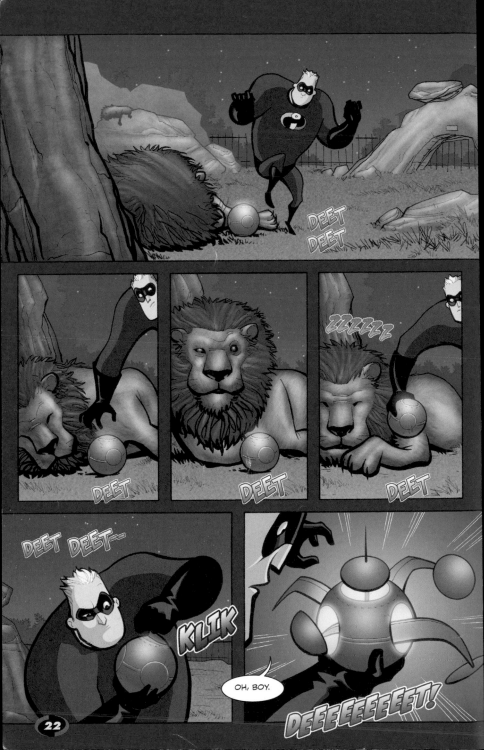

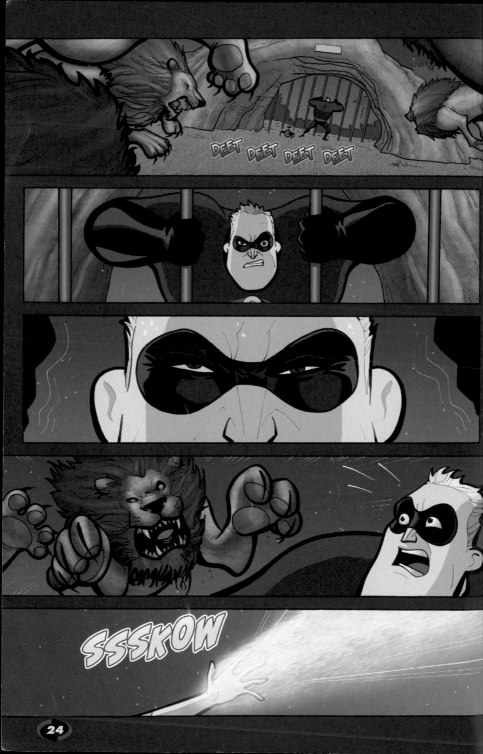

DEETDEETDEE...*

DID SOMEONE CALL FOR **FROZONE?**

CHAPTER TWO

THE GRILL *I GAVE* YOU?

HEY! CAN WE--

--CAN WE STAY ON *MY* PROBLEMS, PLEASE?

FAIR ENOUGH. HOW LONG HAS THIS LITTLE *POWER OUTAGE* BEEN GOING ON?

I FIRST NOTICED IT ABOUT TWO WEEKS AGO. DO YOU REMEMBER THE *SILVERLINE COMMUTER TRAIN?*

"THE 4:14? THE ONE THAT NEARLY CRASHED INTO THE *STATION* A COUPLE WEEK'S *BACK?*"

THE BRAKES ARE OUT!

THE BRAKES ARE OUT!

"THAT'S
THE ONE."

FLUMP

OKAY... YOU CAN *DO* THIS... YOU CAN *DO* THIS...

TIMING'S *CRITICAL* HERE, KIDS, SO WHEN I SAY "MOVE," YOU *HUSTLE!*

SCHOOL BUS

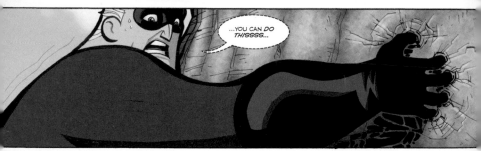

...YOU CAN *DO* TH/SSSS...

EVERYTHING'S GONNA BE *ALL RIGHT,* GUYS! MOVE *QUICKLY* BUT *QUIETLY,* 'KAY? *TIPTOE!*

OOPS!

TONK TONK

CHAPTER THREE

--TWO CREATURES APPEARED OUT OF *NOWHERE* TO TERRORIZE *THREE PINES MALL!*

ALL RIGHT, EVERYONE! WE HAVE A *CITY* TO SAVE!

LET'S *GO!*

WHAT?

NO *WAY!*

NO *POWERS,* NO *ACTION!*

YOU ARE *GROUNDED!*

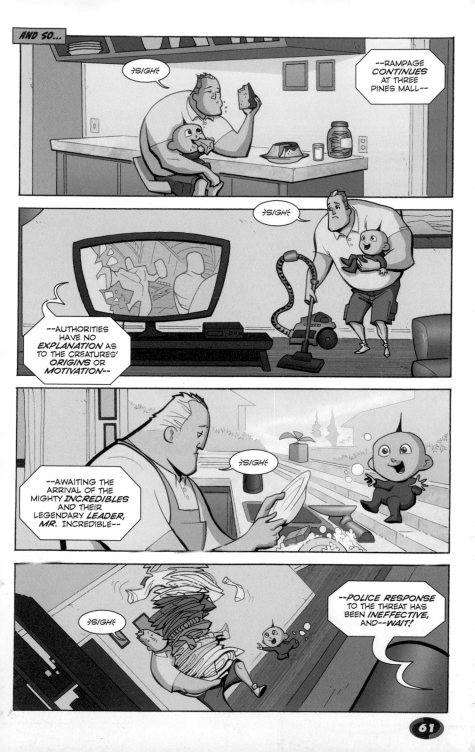

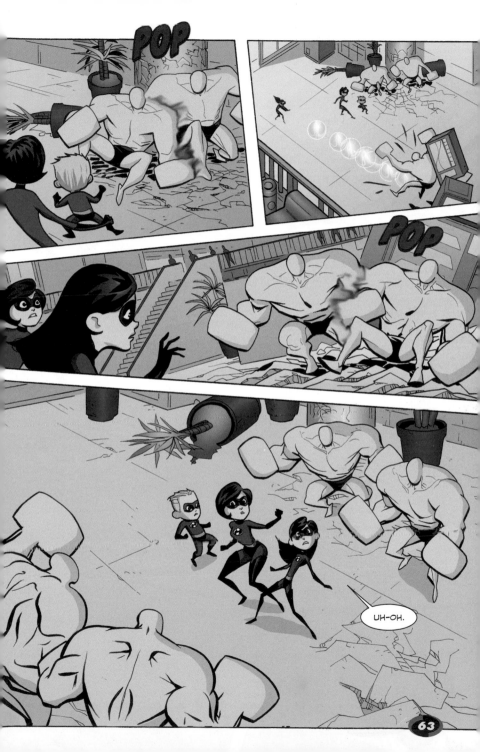

MOM, IT *WORKED* JUST LIKE YOU *SAID!* THEY'RE ALL *BOTTLED UP*--

--AND AT THE MERCY OF THE GREAT AND POWERFUL *DASH!*

*MUU*HAHAHAHA!

GLOATING IS FOR *VILLAINS*, DASH.

SORRY.

LET'S GET YOUR *DAD* ON THE PHONE--

I'M SURE HE'S DYING TO KNOW HOW THIS ALL TURNED OUT.

--COMING TO YOU LIVE FROM THE SIGHT OF THE INCREDIBLES' *LATEST VICTORY!*

NO ONE KNOWS AS YET WHAT THESE MONSTERS *WERE* OR WHERE THEY *CAME* FROM-- BUT THE *REAL* QUESTION IS--

--*WHERE* IS MR. *INCREDIBLE?*

"IT'S ABOUT *HELEN!*"

CHAPTER FOUR

"DAD SAYS WE HAVE TO LIVE 'AWAY FROM IT ALL' FOR A WHILE SO NOBODY ASKS TOO MANY QUESTIONS ABOUT MOM.

"WE WERE AFRAID WE WERE GONNA HAVE TO PUT HER IN A ZOO AT FIRST, BUT SHE'S STILL PRETTY SMART.

"SHE'S TRYING TO MAKE ALL THIS UP TO US BY STILL DOING AS MUCH MOM STUFF AS SHE CAN.

"TURNS OUT SHE'S STILL A GREAT COOK.

"NO MORE DRIVING US TO SCHOOL, THOUGH."